Pops

Wise Publications
London/New York/Paris/Sydney

Exclusive Distributors:
Music Sales Limited
8/9 Frith Street, London W1V 5TZ, England.
Music Sales Pty Limited
120 Rothschild Avenue, Rosebery, NSW 2018, Australia.

This book © Copyright 1992 by
Wise Publications
Order No.AM89939
ISBN 0-7119-3089-9

Music engraved by Interactive Sciences Limited, Gloucester
Cover designed by Hutton Staniford
Music arranged by Stephen Duro
Compiled by Peter Evans

Photographs courtesy of:
Ace/Benelux

Music Sales' complete catalogue lists thousands of titles and is free from your local music shop, or direct from Music Sales Limited. Please send a cheque/postal order for £1.50 for postage to: Music Sales Limited, Newmarket Road, Bury St. Edmunds, Suffolk IP33 3YB.

Your Guarantee of Quality:

As publishers, we strive to produce every book to the highest commercial standards.

All the music has been freshly engraved and the book has been carefully designed to minimise awkward page turns and to make playing from it a real pleasure.

Particular care has been given to specifying acid-free, neutral-sized paper which has not been elemental chlorine bleached but produced with special regard for the environment. Throughout, the printing and binding have been planned to ensure a sturdy, attractive publication which should give years of enjoyment.

If your copy fails to meet our high standards, please inform us and we will gladly replace it.

Printed in the United Kingdom by
Halstan & Co Limited, Amersham, Buckinghamshire.

(Everything I Do) I Do It For You

Words & Music by Bryan Adams, Michael Kamen & Robert John 'Mutt' Lange

Moderately

2. Look into your heart
   You will find there's nothin' there to hide
   Take me as I am, take my life
   I would give it all, I would sacrifice.

   Don't tell me it's not worth fightin' for
   I can't help it, there's nothin' I want more
   You know it's true, everything I do
   I do it for you.

Wind Of Change

Words & Music by Klaus Meine

Verse 3: D.S.

2. The world is closing in
   Did you ever think
   That we could be so close, like brothers
   The future's in the air
   I can feel it everywhere
   Blowing with the wind of change.

3. Walking down the street
   Distant memories
   Are buried in the past forever
   I follow the Moskva
   Down to Gorky Park
   Listening to the wind of change.

Love Hurts

Words & Music by Boudleaux Bryant

Into The Groove

Words & Music by Madonna Ciccone & Steve Bray

Now I   know   you're   mine.   Now I   know   you're   mine.

Now   I   know   you're   mine.   Get   in - to   the   groove—

— boy, you've got to prove—— your love to— me.—

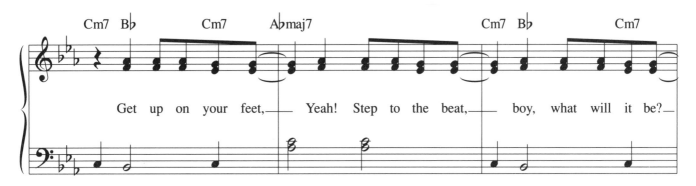

Get   up   on   your feet,—— Yeah! Step to the beat,—— boy, what will it be?—

⊕ Coda

D.%̸ al Coda

_____

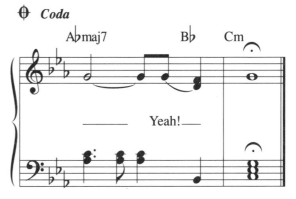

—— Yeah!——

Fool If You Think It's Over

Words & Music by Chris Rea

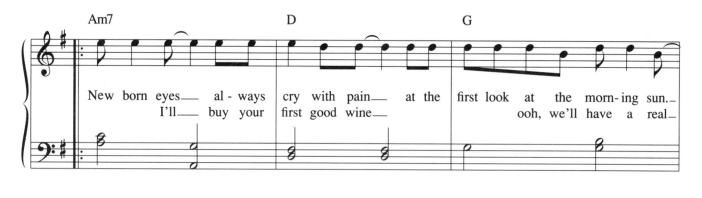

New born eyes— al - ways cry with pain— at the first look at the morn- ing sun.—
I'll buy your first good wine— ooh, we'll have a real—

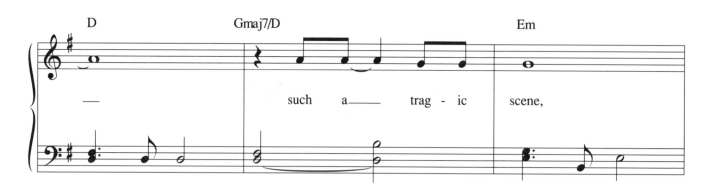

— good time— Fool if you think it's ov - er, it's just be -
and save your cry - ing for the

gun.
day.

Miss Teen - age dream,—

— such a— trag - ic scene,

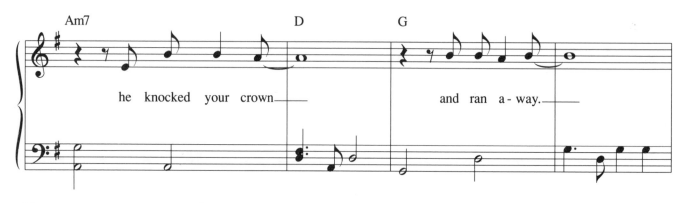

he knocked your crown— and ran a - way.—

First wound of pride____ but how you cried____ and cried.____

but save your tears____ you've years and years.____

New born eyes____ al - ways cry with pain____ at the

first look at the morn - ing sun.____ Fool, if you think it's ov -

____ er, it's just be - gun.

Song For Guy

By Elton John

Moderately

22

We Don't Talk Anymore

Words & Music by Alan Tarney

Another Day In Paradise

Words & Music by Phil Collins

par - a - dise,____ Oh think twice, 'cos it's a-

no - ther day for you,____ you and me in par - a - dise.____

To Coda ✛ | 1. | 2.

Oh Lord,____ is there no - thing more a - ny - bo - dy

28

can do,___ oh_____ Lord___ there must be

some - thing you___ can say.___

D.%. al Coda

Coda

You and me in par - a - dise.___

2. He walks on, doesn't look back,
   he pretends he can't hear her.
   Starts to whistle as he crosses the street,
   seems embarrassed to be there.

3. She calls out to the man in the street,
   he can see she's been crying.
   She's got blisters on the soles of her feet,
   she can't walk, but she's trying.

4. You can tell from the lines on her face,
   you can see that she's been there.
   Probably been moved on from every place
   'cause she didn't fit in there.

The Power Of Love

Words & Music by C. deRouge, G. Mende, J. Rush & S. Applegate

Endless Love

Words & Music by Lionel Richie

The Lady In Red

Words & Music by Chris De Burgh

He Ain't Heavy . . . He's My Brother

Words by Bob Russell, Music by Bobby Scott

Holding Back The Years

Words by Mick Hucknall, Music by Mick Hucknall/Neil Moss

Medium tempo

Bright Eyes

Words & Music by Mike Batt

In The Air Tonight

Words & Music by Phil Collins

2/94 (17288)